KING OF THE CIRCUS

Macmillan
McGraw-Hill
New York Farmington

The circus was on its way up the river to McGregor, Iowa, by boat. The whole town was waiting. Women hummed to themselves as they hung out clean clothes for their families to wear to the tent. Men talked on street corners about cannon-ball jugglers and clowns. Boys and girls remembered the last Dan Rice Circus and called out to each other, "Are you going to get to go?"

Otto Ringling, twelve years old, walked along Main Street and figured that he could drift around in the crowd and slip unnoticed under the tent. He stopped at the General Store and looked at the window poster of "Lizzie—the Baby Bareback Rider." How could this little girl do tricks while standing on the back of a horse?

"She's probably a midget," Otto said to Mr. Foley, the storekeeper.

"No," said Mr. Foley, "the girl is only six years old. Anyway, that's what Dick Clark wrote to his mother."

Dick Clark had gone to school with Otto's big brother, Al. Now he had a perch act in the Dan Rice Circus. To Otto, traveling with a circus seemed the best possible life,

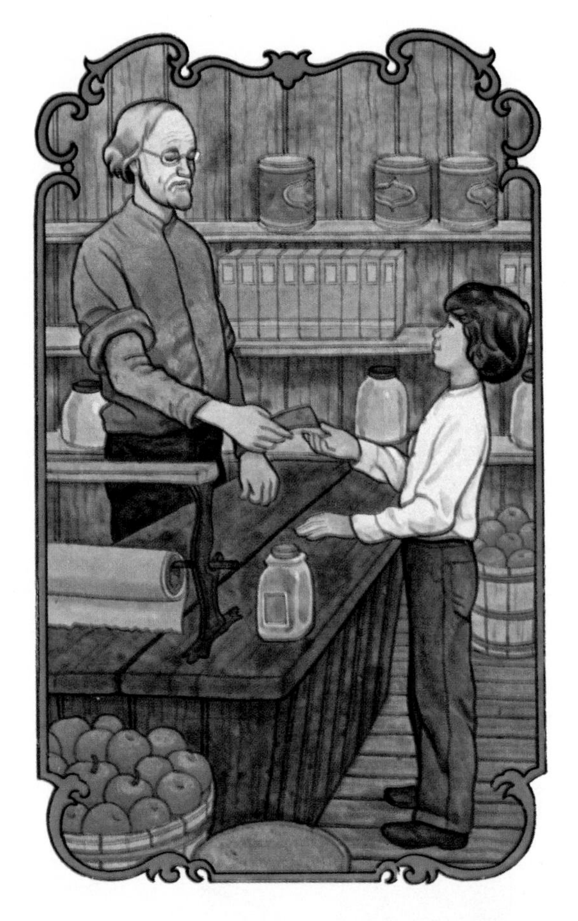

and he wondered if he could work in a perch act. "What's a perch act?" he asked.

"One fellow carries a long pole that has a platform or perch on top, and another fellow stands on his head on the perch," said Mr. Foley.

Otto thought of his eighteen-year-old brother Al, who was a good acrobat. "Step right up," he said, imagining himself as the ringmaster, "and see mighty Al Ringling stand on his head on the perch." He told Mr. Foley that his brother Gus, who was sixteen, could carry the pole.

"The circus is no place for your brothers," said Mr. Foley. "They're born harness-makers. Why, the harness Gus mended for me last week is as good as your Pa could do." Then, remembering that he hadn't paid for the harness repair, he gave Otto a dollar and a quarter for his Pa. "Here," he said, "this money I owe will take all you boys to the circus."

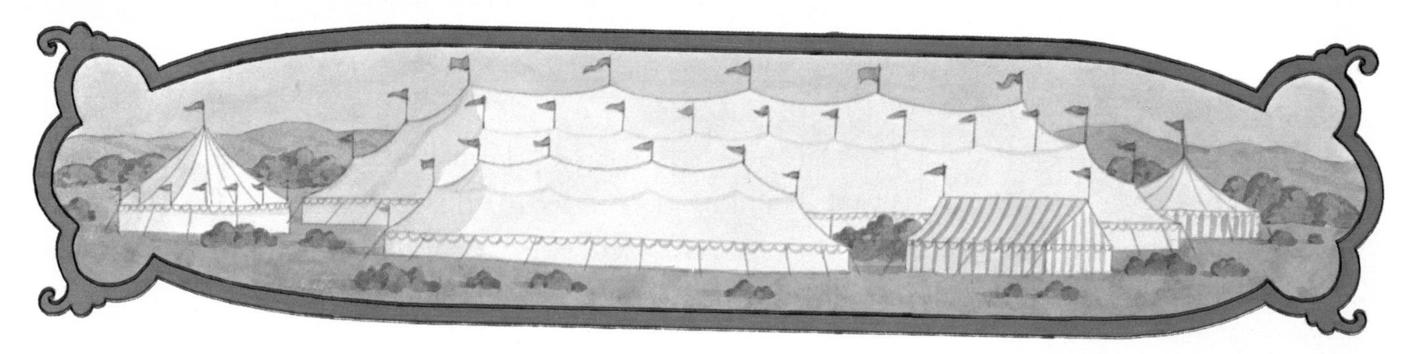

"I'll have to figure another way to get to the circus," Otto said. "We'll be using this to buy more leather for harnesses."

"You're a smart boy," said Mr. Foley, "so don't go running off with any circus. Anyway, who wants to hang around with pickpockets?"

The shopkeeper began taking apples, belt buckles, canes, horse whips, and tobacco from the tops of his counters and putting them away in boxes. "When the circus comes, I hide everything. A lot of people up to no good drift around in the crowd."

Otto thought of his plan to sneak into the tent. "I see what you mean," he said.

"A lot of people stay away from the circus," said the storekeeper, "because they don't want to have their pockets picked."

"The circus should hire policemen to catch pickpockets," Otto said. "Then more people would come, and the circus would make more money."

"You're such a good businessman," said Mr. Foley, "that I think you could run this store."

"It's a very nice store," said Otto, "but what I'd like to run is a circus."

As Otto walked along the river from Mr. Foley's store to his father's shop, farm boys were hitching their horses and getting ready to spend the night. Their laughter filled the air as they talked of waking up to see the circus boat unload. "See you at four o'clock in the morning," one of the boys called to Otto.

Otto burst into the shop where Al, Gus, and Papa were working on separate parts of a harness. Mama was there also.

"The boat's bringing elephants, horses, camels, and bears," said Otto. "It's like Noah's Ark."

"It's not like Noah's Ark," said Mr. Ringling. "Circus people are bums. They run Sunday shows and bring gamblers to town." He said the boys should stay away from the river.

Otto got a sudden glint in his eyes. "I could tell the farm boys with horses about our harnesses. A lot of boys are sleeping down there in their wagons," said Otto.

Mama smiled. This boy was different from the others. When she and Papa had first come here, Al and Gus were in school or working with Papa, and she was usually in the house with the babies. Otto had spent most of his time near the dock where loggers, farmers, and trappers did business with buyers and shippers. Otto had listened and learned from them. He had picked up their ways.

"Please let me go," Otto said.

"OK," said Papa. "I guess it would be good to have them know about us."

Mama thought of the little boys in the house who also wanted to see the circus. "Maybe we should let all the boys go to the boat," she said to Papa. "They're good children."

"Take your brothers along, too," Papa said to Al, who nodded and then headed for the house, turning a double flip-flop on the way. Before sunrise tomorrow, he and his brothers would be watching the circus come in.

The town of McGregor was black and cold and foggy when Al led all of his brothers but Henry, who was just a baby, to the river. Al was eighteen. Then, there was Gus, sixteen; Otto, twelve; Alfred Theodore (called Alf T.), eight; Charlie, six; and John, four.

The boys huddled together. They could hear the music of the steam calliope long before they could see the boat. As the music grew louder, they moved closer to the water. The little boys jumped up and down as the boat came

around the bend with torches flaming on every deck.

In the flickering light, the boys could see, next to the big boat, a barge filled with chariots. Bells clanged as the big boat touched shore. Soon, three pairs of horses came down the gangplank. They were quickly hitched to the red and gold chariots, which they pulled off down the road to the circus grounds.

As the day grew lighter, two bears with rings in their noses came down the plank; then, two camels; and then, more horses. Finally, came an animal that seemed as large as the boat itself. It had a long trunk and smelled stronger than a horse, better than a skunk, and cleaner than a dog.

"An elephant," said little John, looking at the great, grey animal which came down the plank with a man on its back. The man looked like a ghost.

"Anyone know August Ringling?" the man called.

"He's our father," the boys called back.

The ghost slid down from the elephant and spoke to Al, who recognized Dick Clark. Like a flock of sparrows, the smaller Ringling boys swooped around Al's friend, the circus man, who carried a belt over his arm and a long pole in his hand.

Dick explained that he had broken his belt and that without it he couldn't do the perch act. Al told Dick that they could fix his belt at the harness shop. "Just follow us," he said.

The boys tumbled and danced around Dick until they reached Papa's place, which was dark. Several boys had followed along and crowded around the door to see what was up.

Otto lit a kerosene lamp, and the Ringlings and the others in the door watched as Dick buckled on a wide belt. In its front was a torn pouch, called a "socket," which was meant to hold the pole. "If the pole slips, the man up top will fall," said Dick.

Gus, who was the best harness-maker, took the belt over by the lamp to fix it. John, who was a plump show-off, showed Dick how he could stand on his hands; and Charlie, who was a wiry boy, stood on his head. The boys told Dick that Al was the best acrobat in town and kept urging him to flip-flop, but Al kept saying, "Ssshhhh."

The crowd was pressing in, so the boys moved outside the shop. When Gus had mended the socket, he brought out the belt. Dick put the pole in it and asked Al if he would like to go up and stand on his head. Al shinned up but slid down again as Mama and Papa came toward the shop.

"Everybody in the county will know about your harness shop now," Otto told Papa.

Alf T. gave Otto a push. "He didn't have anything to do with getting the crowd here," Alf T. told Papa, who looked puzzled. "The people followed Dick" He ran over and asked Al to lift him up on the perch so he could show Mama the perch act. As Alf T. swung his legs from the little platform above Al, Papa looked stern, but Mama laughed. And when Dick came over to ask what he owed, Mama said, "Nothing."

Dick said that if he couldn't pay he would like to give all the Ringlings a pass to the circus. Al clapped Dick on the arm. The little boys jumped around. But Gus said this would be a big harness day, and he would stay here.

Much to everyone's surprise, Mama said, "People will have to wait to have their harnesses fixed. Papa will work alone today, I will stay with the baby, and all the rest of you will go to the circus."

The Ringling brothers never forgot what happened in the tent that day.

Each girl in the circus rode standing up on a horse the way Lizzie was riding in the picture. And each one had a man partner who also stood up. Around and around they went in a parade of twin horses. All the girls wore pink and green leafy dresses that floated up and down. And the men wore long tights and bowed to the people as the girls blew kisses. And all the time, the ringmaster kept the horses moving right around in time to the music.

Clowns in those days stood by the ringmaster in the middle of the ring, talking to the audience and cracking jokes. The clown in this circus was Dan Rice, the owner of the show. He told funny stories and got a bear and an elephant to dance.

Dick Clark came out with his pole. Dick's partner on the perch stood on his head and bounced a ball on his feet. Then, Dick rode a bicycle while his partner did a handstand. Dan Rice told the crowd that the Ringlings in the front row had mended Dick's belt. Everyone clapped, and Al, Gus, and Otto looked down but felt happy.

Then Lizzie came out wearing a little, white standout skirt and a pink bow in her hair. She stood on a great, white horse that raced faster and faster around the ring. When she came to a scarf held high across her pathway by two tall men, the drums rolled. Otto held his breath as

Lizzie jumped high in the air, twirling as she came down over the scarf onto the back of the moving horse. Otto and everybody else cheered.

Finally, it was time for the trapeze artists, who were supposed to work *without* a net. But now, as they climbed up the pole to the trapeze at the top of the tent, Dan said there *would* be a net. The people on the bleachers resented being taken in, and they began to stamp their feet and boo. One tall man in a straw hat ran out from the crowd and shook his fists at Dan. "You are cheating us," he bellowed. Then he called up to the trapeze artists that anyone could do what they were doing *with* a net.

Dan tried to push the tall man away, but the man fell into the net. He bounced high, with his arms and legs flying, and was caught by a man hanging by his knees from a trapeze. Then, suddenly, the tall man was being swung and bounced from one trapeze artist to another. As the crowd screamed with laughter and fear, two men took away the net.

Even before the wild-acting fellow lost his coat and pants and began swinging through the air in tights, Otto knew that he was part of the show. "He's one of the tall men who held the scarf for Lizzie," he told his brothers. Now the people who had been angry about the net

screamed with laughter. "They don't mind being fooled when the joke makes the act better," said Al.

After the ladies came back to throw kisses, the show ended, and the Ringlings left the tent. None of the brothers would be the same again.

Old-time circus people say that you can't get along in the circus unless your parents were circus people or unless you have gypsy blood. The Ringlings were different. Except for their tall crazy-acting grandfather on their mother's side who had served with Napoleon and called out "Long live the Emperor" whenever he saw a horse with a plume, they had no dramatic relatives. They did have an asset that many circus people don't have, however, and that was the ability to divide up work to get things done. They had learned this from their hard-working German father in his harness shop. "You make the checkrein," he would say to one boy. "And you make the bellyband," he would say to another. "And I'll make the collar." Working this way, a harness would soon be finished.

On the day after the circus, Al told all of his brothers (even little John) to meet him up on the high bluff behind their house. Standing there in Iowa, they could see three other states: down the river, they could see Illinois; across, they could see Wisconsin; up, they could see Minnesota.

"How would you like to have a circus and go to all four states?" Al asked his brothers.

The five other Ringling boys said, "That's great," and "When do we start?" and "Let's go!"

Al told his brothers that it would take a lot of work to get a circus started, but if they worked as they had always worked with Papa, they could do it. "Each Ringling will do what he can do best," said Al, "and we will give our first performance three weeks from now."

The brothers said that Al, who was oldest and knew the most about circuses, should be manager of the show.

Gus had trained his hunting dog to bring a stick to the fire, so he would be the animal trainer.

Alf T. could draw, so he would make posters.

Charlie was a "born musician," so he would be in charge of the band.

John was the funniest. He would be in charge of making people laugh.

That left Otto, who said, "I'm the best in arithmetic."

"So you can be business manager," said Al, giving him a little shove, "as if you didn't know."

For the next few weeks, the boys worked like real circus hands. Al figured out some acts, and each night after he had worked with Papa, he directed his brothers in what they were to do. Before the rest of the family was up in the morning, Al went to the backyard where he walked a tightrope, juggled plates, and swung by his knees from a trapeze.

Gus made a grey trunk for a stray goat and began teaching this "elephant" to walk through a hoop and take a bow. Alf T. made a poster for Mr. Foley's store. And Charlie borrowed a fife, a trumpet, and a uniform from Cap Brown who had been a soldier in the Civil War.

Mama worked nearly as hard as the boys. She made a white clown suit with black dots for John, and she patched up Papa's old long underwear for Al to wear as tights. She made plumes and tails for Alf T. and Charlie to wear in their "High-Stepping Act." And she collected blankets and sheets for the tent.

A week before the circus, Gus set up tentpoles in the pasture where Dan Rice had put on his show. Gus figured fifty people could fit inside the "tent" once he got his blankets nailed up.

When Al was wondering how much money this would bring, Otto said, "Five hundred pins."

"Pins!" Al said. "Are you out of your head? This is a real show!"

"You must be crazy," Gus joined in. "Pins, my foot!" He said that Al's show was going to be as good as the Dan Rice Circus, and when Otto said it wasn't going to be nearly that good, Gus shoved him down on the ground. Al stopped the fight but said, "No pins!"

Otto was talking in a loud voice as he struggled to his feet. "I've got a reason for pins," Otto said, "and as long as I'm business manager, that's what it's going to be!"

Al gave in. "We will do the show for pins."

Otto thought of this first show as a dress rehearsal. His aim was to pack the tent and give everyone a good time. The money would come next time.

For days before the circus, Alf T. paraded around with a picture of an elephant with the message: BIG SHOW —10 PINS. And Otto gave a free pass to a little girl cousin who agreed to ask everyone she saw for three pins "to go with my seven so I can see the circus." She more than earned her pass!

On the morning of Circus Day there was a big parade. Al turned handsprings all the way down Main Street. High-stepping Alf T. and Charlie followed in plumes and tails, pulling John, dressed as a clown, in a red and gold wagon. Gus kept throwing out a stick printed with the words, COME TO THE CIRCUS; his dog kept fetching it back. And Otto, wearing the elephant sign, pounded a drum.

The boys packed sixty people into their topless tent. The spectators sat on a circle of straw, and the boys worked in the ring.

Al's acrobatic stunts turned out to be as good as many in the Dan Rice Circus, and he got loud applause. Charlie, in Cap Brown's Civil War uniform, played a sad old war song on Cap's trumpet. The band consisted of Charlie

on the fife, Alf T. on the mouth harp, and John on the comb. They played marching-band songs, and the crowd clapped in time to the music.

Finally, Otto gave a dramatic pound to his drum and introduced the "elephant act." Out came Charlie in a gold paper crown followed by the goat in elephant disguise. As Charlie took a low bow, the "elephant," who was supposed to push a ball through a large hoop, butted Charlie through instead. Charlie's crown went flying, and the crowd roared.

After that, everything got a laugh. Al dropped a plate while juggling, and the crowd loved it. Shep, the trick dog, fell off the perch that Gus had made for him on top of a pole. The crowd whistled. During the band's last number, Charlie rubbed the seat of his pants and the crowd yelled. It was a great day.

The next morning Otto divided his 600 straight pins into thirty piles of twenty. Then he pinned twenty straight pins on thirty separate sheets of paper. Knowing that Mr. Foley could sell each sheet for two cents, Otto offered to sell him each sheet for a penny. Mr. Foley bought the thirty sheets. Otto presented Al with thirty cents, which was worth about as much in those days as three dollars is worth now.

Otto told Al that everybody was talking about the show and that now they could charge more.

The boys charged a penny a ticket for their next two shows and a nickel for the fourth. Al was getting better on the trapeze and tightrope. Charlie could play five instruments. And Gus made a bigger tent, which Otto filled. At the summer's end they had $8.37.

They spent the money for a very old pony. Now with the pony, a wild goat, and their trick dog, they needed an even bigger tent. Gus made it during the winter, and they looked forward to a new season.

Next summer, Al balanced a broom on his chin, turned double flip-flops from a high trapeze, and walked a tightrope above the crowd. Gus built a platform for the back of the pony, and Alf T. and Charlie wore white underwear, painted their faces white, and posed on the platform as statues. At the end of the summer, the boys had made $25. But now came bad luck.

Hard times hit McGregor. No one had money for a circus—or even for a harness. Papa Ringling could not pay for leather or keep up payments on his house and shop. He lost everything and was forced to move to Baraboo, Wisconsin, to start again. When he and Mama had a new

baby—a girl named Ida—all the boys had to go to work.

Now when the boys talked about the circus, Papa turned white with anger. "I don't want my boys to be bums," he shouted, "or to keep putting on backyard shows. Get jobs like men." All the boys but Al did what he ordered.

Al, an excellent acrobat and juggler, worked out an act that made him famous—balancing a plow on the point of his chin. He got a job with a traveling "hall show" that put on acts in town halls.

Both John and Henry did odd jobs after school. John kept running away from home, and Otto was always sent to find him.

When John was twelve, he ran away to a rooming house where Otto found him mixing up a batch of cleansing powder to sell door to door. Otto helped him sell ten packages and took the money home to Papa, which saved John from getting a licking. The next time he ran away, John joined a tent show as a ticket taker, but after he'd done his job, the manager wouldn't pay him. John wrote to Otto asking what to do. Otto told him to take the money from the cashbox and, with a policeman, go to the manager and tell him that he, John, had taken his own pay. John did this, and the manager could do nothing.

Al came home for Christmas and worked up a "Concert and Comedy" road show with Alf T. and Charlie, who had been playing in a dance band. When the trio left town, Gus, who was happy making harnesses, and Henry, who was too young to go along, wished them well. But Otto and John were dejected. They still wanted that family circus.

Train wrecks, cyclones, and hotel fires (which they read about in their brothers' letters) seemed romantic to Otto and John, who were tired of harnesses. Finally, John took off on a midnight train to join his brothers. He took along a joke book and an idea for a "Carnival of Fun."

Otto kept pushing for a Ringling Brothers' Circus, but his brothers wrote that a circus had to have a tent, wagons, animals, acts, costumes, and a band. Where were they going to get the money? When Al wrote that he was going to marry a seamstress and was looking for a job as an acrobat, Otto knew this was the time to act.

"Some way I am going to get that circus started," he told Papa in the harness shop.

"Circus people are bums," Papa began in the same old way, but Otto paid no attention.

"I will send you money," he told Papa, "but I will never make another harness."

Papa sensed that this time Otto was really going to have his circus. "All right," he said, "but promise that you won't have shows on Sunday!"

Papa and his old-time ways! Otto was about to protest when he realized that closing the show on Sunday might be good for business. It might convince mothers that the Ringlings were not "bums" and could be counted on for a good, clean, family show. "No Sunday show," Otto promised Papa. Then, he went to the banker and told him of his plan to start a circus that would have no pick-pockets and would keep the Sabbath holy. The banker lent him enough to pay for a tent that would hold 600 people.

A jubilant Otto left that night to surprise his brothers, but when he reached their hotel, *he* was surprised. Al had been married the night before to the seamstress, Louise, and the innkeeper had unfairly raised the price of his room. She locked up his trunks (costumes, clothes, and all) in her rooms and refused to give them back until he paid his bill. When Otto walked in, Al was pounding on the innkeeper's locked door.

Otto had just arrived by train, and he knew it would be pulling out any minute. "Fire!" he yelled. "Fire!"

And John hollered through the door to the innkeeper, "You still have time to get out!" The woman came flying out to the arms of John who helped her down the street to safety as his brothers grabbed their trunks and beat it for the station.

The train was moving slowly down the tracks when John jumped to the back platform and waved good-by to the innkeeper who was stamping her feet and shaking her fists. The brothers pounded each other on the back and laughed until they cried.

Nothing could stop them now! They had money, talent, and spirit. And they even had Louise, who wanted to be a snake charmer. They sat together on that train and made plans for a circus that would be the biggest in the world.

The Ringlings had no wild animals, but they hired an old circus clown, Yankee Robinson, to crack jokes. They had no band, but they had Charlie to play eight instruments. And they had Al to defy death at the top of the tent and Louise to wear a boa constrictor around her waist.

For their first performance, in Baraboo, the Ringlings charged a quarter for the main show, a nickel for Charlie's concert afterward, and another nickel for the sideshow where John did tricks with a trained pig. When Otto counted the cash after their first day and night in Baraboo, they had $460.

The brothers packed tent, poles, seats, and other trappings into nine carts driven by farm boys, much like those back in McGregor who slept by the river. The boys had been invited by Otto to come with their own horses to travel with the Ringlings and see four states.

Yankee Robinson died during their first season, and John became their clown. Rival shows laughed at their "Sunday-School show," but crowds packed their tent. They were stuck in the mud so often they became known as "the mud show." They bought a moth-eaten hyena which they called a "man-eating beast with a blood-chilling laugh."

The circus grew, and in only four years was traveling in a mile-long caravan of red and gold chariots crammed with sixty horses, bears, camels, elephants, peacocks, midgets, snakes, a 600-pound fat lady, and a bearded woman. Then, Otto, who was business manager, bought the circus its own railroad train.

Some say the Ringlings prospered because there were so many to do the work. Henry became ticket master, Gus managed the winter quarters in Baraboo, Al was director, Alf T. got people to come, Charlie got things moved, and John was the scout for new acts.

Once John wired Otto that he had signed up "Lizzie, the Bareback Rider" who was now a lovely equestrienne. Otto met the train with a flock of pigeons dyed pink like the long-ago bow in Lizzie's hair. Some say he never married because Lizzie arrived with a husband.

Actually, Otto had one true love, the circus; and he wanted the Ringlings to have the best. He didn't like competition, so he found a way to buy the Barnum & Bailey Circus, their greatest rival. After that, the one Ringling who had never performed in the circus became its King.

All the artists loved Otto, who had been ring-struck since the age of twelve. When he died, his circus family sent a flower-covered circus wheel to Baraboo. One spoke was missing. The King was gone.

Old-timers say that nothing can ever replace the old Circus Day. And in show business, people say that no story can rival that of the Ringlings who built a backyard show into what was truly the *Greatest Show on Earth.*

RINGLING
BROS
ALF. T. RINGLING
AL. RINGLING
CHAS. RINGLING
JOHN RINGLING
OTTO RINGLING
KINGS
OF THE
CIRCUS
WORLD
COPYRIGHT 1905 BY THE STROBRIDGE LITHO, COMPANY.
CIN'TI & NEW YORK.

RINGLING
BROS
WORLD'S GREATEST SHOWS
250
150
100
150
500
300